●Huntsville

The

Medical Reports

of

John Y. Bassett, M.D.

The Alabama Student

The
MEDICAL REPORTS
of
JOHN Y. BASSETT, M.D.

The Alabama Student

With an Introduction by
DANIEL C. ELKIN, M.D.
Joseph B. Whitehead Professor
of Surgery, Emory University

CHARLES C THOMAS · MCMXLI

CONTENTS

INTRODUCTION

A series of fortuitous circumstances rescued John Y. Bassett from the oblivion to which he seemed otherwise doomed. Osler, in looking over the literature of malarial fevers, chanced upon Bassett's articles in Fenner's *Southern Medical Reports*. He was so fascinated by the charm of these philosophical essays that he set about to piece together his life, largely gathered from the letters which Bassett wrote home during his European tour, and from extracts from the *Reports*. The result was *An Alabama Student*,[1] the most delightful and popular of Osler's many biographical excursions.

There was another, now forgotten, who played an unknowing part in Bassett's rendezvous with fame—Erasmus

[1] *An Alabama Student and Other Biographical Essays* by William Osler, Oxford University Press, 1908. Also see Note on page 62.

Darwin Fenner, a man of considerable ability and of wide but passing influence, particularly in the field of medical journalism. Fenner was the son of a Revolutionary officer, and a native of North Carolina. After graduating at Transylvania, he settled in New Orleans in 1841. Four years later he commenced the publication of *The New Orleans Medical Journal*. In 1856 he was instrumental in organizing the New Orleans School of Medicine, and held the chair of Principles and Practice, and was Dean of its faculty.

With the outbreak of the War between the States, Fenner accompanied the Louisiana troops to Virginia and, at his own expense, organized a hospital at Richmond. He returned to Louisiana in 1861 in order to supervise the forwarding of supplies to the troops in the field. With the fall of New Orleans in 1862 came the order of the Federal Commandant for all to take the oath of allegiance or leave the city. Fenner, an ardent Southerner, took passage to Pascagoula, and thence to Mobile, where he continued the care of the sick and wounded until the end of the war.

With the advent of peace he returned to New Orleans and soon afterwards announced the publication of the *Southern Journal of the Medical Sciences*, with himself as Senior Editor. However, he did not live to see it in print for he died on May 4, 1866, the day of the issue of the first number. It contains a valuable contribution from his pen on the sanitary condition of the city during the period of military occupation. In this Fenner pointed out the decrease in yellow fever and other diseases, and, as much as he hated the Commandant, he was willing to give the devil his due, as he did in the concluding paragraphs of his paper:

From all that precedes, it would appear that Generals Butler[2] and Banks have done for New Orleans what the tyrant Mehemed Ali did for Cairo, and we may yet have occasion to mingle some thanks among the many curses we have heaped upon their heads for their unnecessary severity upon the citizens of New Orleans.

For twenty years we, and some others, have labored to convince the people of New Orleans that the only way to make the city healthy is *to make and keep it clean*. But we have labored in vain. In the mysterious course of events the hand of the tyrant has been brought to our aid, and the results are marvelous. Will our citizens profit by this experience, and continue to enforce their own health ordinances as the federal military authorities enforced them? If they do not, the consequences will surely be deplorable.

But to return to Fenner's connection with Bassett. Disagreement with his fellow editors forced Fenner from the staff of *The New Orleans Medical and Surgical Journal*, and in 1849 and 1850 we find him as the sole editor of the *Southern Medical Reports*. Fenner was firm in his belief that medicine in the South could only be advanced by

[2] This refers to General Benjamin F. Butler of Massachusetts. Although generally called "Beast Butler," he also acquired the title of "Spoon" because of his easy-fingered methods of collecting silver, most of which is said to have found its way as heirlooms to the tables and sideboards of Beacon Hill. He was particularly clever in the infliction of petty atrocities, such as the chaining of Confederate officers to negro convicts, and notorious for his infamous order, issued in New Orleans on May 15, 1862, that if any woman should "insult or show contempt for any officer or soldier of the United States, she shall be regarded and shall be held liable to be treated as a woman of the town plying her avocation."

The most infamous of Yankee generals, Butler was not soon forgotten in the better part of the United States. (*The second sentence of this paragraph has been printed elsewhere and is available until the present supply is exhausted if a written request is addressed to the publisher.*)

Southern journals and Southern schools. A colleague quotes him:

> What does the most cultivated Northern physician know about treating our yellow fever, or pernicious fever or our diarrheas? While I certainly would respect the cultivation of their minds, I confess I'd rather have an intelligent and experienced plantation overseer to treat me with one of these diseases.

Moreover, he believed in the doctrine of the "unity of fevers," and the rôle of the topography in disease. With this in mind he asked the contributors to the *Southern Medical Reports* to record carefully and in detail the topography and meteorology of their communities. Among the contributors was John Y. Bassett of Huntsville, Alabama. Here apparently was Bassett's long hoped-for chance to air his philosophy—his love of truth, his hatred of hypocrisy, of cant and of quackery, and most of all the occasion to put in print his *credo*.

The *Southern Medical Reports* suspended publication after two years because of lack of support. Never widely circulated, these volumes are rare, found only in a few libraries and in private collections. Knowing that Mr. Charles Thomas liked to do things like this, I suggested that he reprint the two reports that they might be available to students. This he has agreed to do, but with the generous stipulation that certain profits which might be derived from their publication be given to the Harvey Cushing Library at Yale. This is altogether fitting since *An Alabama Student* was Dr. Cushing's favorite gift book.

Atlanta, November, 1940.   DANIEL C. ELKIN

The

Medical Reports

of

John Y. Bassett, M.D.

The Alabama Student

ARTICLE I

REPORT ON THE TOPOGRAPHY, CLIMATE AND DISEASES OF MADISON COUNTY, ALA.

This report was accompanied by a beautiful map of Madison County, delineated by the author himself, who certainly must possess considerable talent for drawing. We deeply regret not being able to publish it at this time, on account of the heavy expense. The map was accompanied by a great amount of curious and interesting statistics, a part of which we must take the liberty to exclude as not having any immediate relation to medicine. We shall arrange the first part of his matter somewhat differently from the way in which it was received, and then let the author proceed with his subject in his own way. (Dr. Erasmus Darwin Fenner in *Southern Medical Reports*.)

Huntsville is situated about the middle of Madison County, Alabama, latitude 34° 45′ N., longitude 9° 45′ W., and contains, within the limits of one square mile, about twenty-six hundred inhabitants, of whom a fair proportion are negroes and children.

The county contains 530,000 square acres, of which there are

In ponds, marshes and lands injured by back water.	25,000	acres
In mountains and rivers.	50,000	"
In cultivation	92,000	"
	167,000	"
Remaining in forest	363,000	"
	530,000	"

MINERAL CHARACTER

Limestone in the valleys; in the mountains, red sandstone, coal, and some iron. Water generally cool and pleasant, weak limestone; temperature, from 60° to 65°.

The Tennessee River runs along the entire Southern border of the county; Flynt River and a number of smaller streams intersect it in various parts. There are some considerable mountain elevations in the county, the greatest of which is Monte Sano, near Huntsville.

Height of Monte Sano above Huntsville.	1,090	ft.
" " Huntsville, above Tennessee river, at Ditto's.	86	"
" " Tennessee river, above the sea at Mobile . .	675	"
" " Monte Sano above tide water at Mobile. . .	1,851	"

According to the Census of 1840, the number of inhabitants in Madison County was 26,706:

Consisting of Whites. 12,297
Negro slaves 14,265
" free 144

There are thirty physicians in the county who do an aggregate of about thirty thousand dollars of good practice annually; to which may be added ten to twenty per cent for charity.

There are six irregular or nondescript practitioners, who claim an aggregate practice of six thousand dollars annually; but there is no possibility of approximating truth in this direction.

Of the thirty physicians in the county, six reside in Huntsville, and do about twelve thousand dollars worth of good practice. We have also a German Root-Doctor, a Homœopathist, a Steam Doctor and several negro Faith-Doctors. I have no means of ascertaining the amount of their practice, though it is certain that the last who comes generally does a respectable amount for a longer or shorter time, which depends upon his individual tact and church-membership.

There is about ten thousand dollars worth of medicines sold annually in the county (including about 80 pounds of calomel and 1,000 ounces of quinine[1]) of which about $5,000 is quackery. I have no means of ascertaining the number of deaths, births and marriages.

[1] Our druggists sell 100 pounds of calomel and 1400 ounces of quinine annually.

SEASONS

Winter.—We have a little snow every winter, and occasionally it lays from a few hours to a few days; ice sufficient for summer consumption, from half an inch to an inch and a half in thickness but, owing to the bad construction of our ice-houses, it generally melts by the latter part of August. Within the last twenty years china trees have been twice killed by frost.

Spring.—This season is generally wet; frosts late enough to injure both cotton and corn. In the last spring the entire crop of wheat was destroyed by a frost or freeze in the latter part of April.

Summer.—Generally very hot, though not sultry. In the direct rays of the sun, I believe the thermometer would rise to 160° after midday, and fall after midnight, sometimes to 60°, making a variation of 100 degrees in twenty-four hours. It rained every day during the last July averaging, it is supposed, half an inch daily. August generally wet and hot.

Fall.—The latter part clear, cool, dry and the most delightful season of our year.

HISTORICAL SKETCH

There were white men living in Madison County previous to the beginning of the present century. In 1809, the first land sales took place at Nashville, and a portion of these temporary Squatters became permanent Settlers. The most of those who did not procure homes at that time, belonged to a class who, from taste or compulsion, had separated themselves from the whites to live on the trail of the Indians; and who, like tigers and Judases, were not without their use in the mysterious economy of nature. They surpassed the natives in physical force and in genius, and equalled them in ferocity. They had the piratical appetite for gain natural to the English race, which they had cultivated among the whites, and they readily acquired the Indian taste for blood.

Thus, without any particular standard of morals of their own, and having fallen out with that which restrained their christian brethren, they found their interest in adopting the ancient one of Moses and of the Savages among whom they resided—"an eye for an eye" and "blood for blood."

These men, like the fabulous behemouth that lay in the reedy fens of the early world, drinking up the abundant waters and eating down the luxuriant forests to make way for civilization, have left little more than a vague tradition of their existence and exploits, the latter of which has been so embellished that the former already begins to be doubted.

Such a race leave but short records of their diseases— where bloodshed is always epidemic and every man his own surgeon; the few that recover feel grateful to none and hang no "votive tablets" on the natural columns of their forests—and when a missionary or a novelist is the only historian, it would puzzle Hippocrates himself to collate the cases; but, as most things, as well as lions, track the earth in some manner as they pass over it, these early squatters have also made their mark.

CASE

While digging a cellar, a few years back, on the public square, the workmen opened a cavern that communicated with the spring. They discovered a number of bones; among them lay at least one human skeleton with a broken skull, and a broken bottle, from which the ardent and fiery spirits had alike escaped. The skull was an Indian's and cleft with a hatchet or heavy knife from over the left eye to the crown; lesser marks of this weapon than the fatal one indicate resistance, and his having been hidden in a cave proclaims that a white man slew him; Indians do not hide their dead.

After the land sales a better class of men, owners and cultivators of the soil, settled in and about Huntsville, and physicians located amongst them. These were principally young Virginians of good families, who had never offered for graduation, or who had been rejected by the Philadelphia and Baltimore Schools (for there was a time when our Medical Schools did reject some), and whose out-fit in life generally consisted of a pretty fair education, a genteel suit of clothes, a good horse and a mulatto servant; and whose object in life, to judge from their habitudes, was like that of our young preachers: to marry, and quit a profession they never loved, because they never knew. Though few medical facts of value could be expected *from* these gentlemen, their neighbors have preserved in the traditional archives of the village some interesting notes *of* their practice.

CASE

A man was knocked down on an election day, and lay senseless. Dr. H. forced his way through the crowd and seized the wrist of the patient. (The radial artery dividing high up, dodged the doctor's thumb by passing over the back of the hand.) Having no history of the case he pronounced it "Apoplexy." "Is he dangerous?" said the Sheriff. "I pronounce him a dead man," said the Doctor. "Did you say that in reference to me?" asked the patient, raising and reaching for his mashed hat.

The diseases of this period were deadly, particularly about the margin of Tennessee River and Indian Creek; men frequently died in the second or third chill. The common practice, from what I can learn, was to give an emetic of antimony, follow it with 20 grains calomel and 20 of jalap; upon this a dose of West India castor oil; next day an ounce of bark and a grain or two of opium. Those who lived after it reflected great credit on the doctor, and gained him the reputation of being a "bold practitioner."

During the second lustrum of our political existence, the intellectual and professional character of our practising physicians gradually improved; there were men of proper education and undoubted genius occasionally among them; but unfortunately there was a wild, speculating, and gambling spirit abroad in the country, and the morals of the card table were introduced at the bed-side of the patient, and into the office of the preceptor—successful tricks unbecoming the dignity of the profession were called "smart," and gentlemen did not deem it disgraceful to gamble with their own pupils.

CASE

Dr. H. arrived a stranger at the Planter's Hotel; the landlord introduced him to a sick traveller, sinking in a typhoid fever. "He should be bled," said Dr. H. "Bled," echoed the attendant physician. "Yes, bled! or he'll die." This gentleman accomplished two objects with this short sentence: he disgusted the attendant, and captivated the patient. With some difficulty he managed to stain the bed clothes with a little blood, then gave hot brandy toddy, and pursued a vigorous and judicious tonic course of treatment. He charged this patient $500 for ten days services, and lost it with him at cards in less than half as many hours. This gentleman had professional skill and tact enough to have taken and kept the lead anywhere in this region at that time, and been an honor and benefit to society. He charged high for his services, yet made nothing; he played skillfully at cards, yet lost everything.

It is true that the head of the medical profession in this county in itself is but a low elevation, and has been occupied by men who have had as much life sacrificed to their transient reputation as has for the same period been crushed out under the wheels of a Juggernaut. But, about this period of our medical history Doctor Thomas Fearn, without aspiring to it, by common consent occupied this position, which as long as he remained in the profession he retained by the exercise of qualifications that would

have placed him in the same relative position in much larger fields of operation, and better educated communities. And though he did not travel up the tangled path of medical eminence without having "his heel bruised," this consent at length became so unanimous, both within and without the profession, that even respectable men were laughed at for presuming to compete with him.

CASE

A row at the "Bell." A man stabbed. Dr. O. called in. He had been introduced as an accomplished surgeon by a political or a religious party, and praised like a new preacher; he found the wound too deep for him, and half a dozen lay brothers as bloody as "Septembrisers" who were holding and helping. The man fainted, a murmur ran through the crowd. Fearn's name was mentioned. The doctor probed away and said nothing; he fainted again, and the doctor, reeking with blood, pronounced the wound mortal! There was a universal shout for Fearn. The man who had commenced this operation with a Bowie knife, feeling some interest in the issue, was bringing Fearn to his assistance, who understanding the entire nature of the case, had armed himself with an Assilini's forceps (a slight modification of which the English call "Liston's Bull-Dog," instead of his petty larceny); with this he seized the bleeding vessel, and without assistant, or scarcely soiling his fingers, secured it. When he was about to depart the patient asked him at what time he would see him again. "You may come to my office in the morning," said the Doctor, "and some of the young men will attend to you."

The influence of this gentleman's reputation upon the profession was favorable to the residence of thorough-bred physicians in the neighborhood, many of whom he had been directly instrumental in educating; another consequence followed, quackery and empiricism abated. Although quackery is indigenous in the human heart, like thieving and lying, and always will exist, yet it flourishes in the indirect ratio of the science and general qualifications of the regular part of the profession. When regular, and extensively patronised physicians, armed with all requisite diplomas and the experience of years, suffer themselves to grow so dull in diagnosis as to bleed a typhoid patient half an hour before death in the evening, that they had been stimulating through the day, or so far forget or compromise the dignity of their high calling as to practise "Mesmerism," or prescribe "Mother's Relief!" to a parturient woman, men of smaller pretentions, and more professional pride, or better information, should not, and do not wonder at quackery springing up around such like mushrooms in a spring morning where a fat cow has lain over night, and warmed the soil for their reception.

CASE

A political doctor was called from the "stump" to extract a bullet from the belly of a friend; after probing and searching for a time, a doctor differing in politics, not of great respectability in his profession, suggested to the surgeon to let the ball alone and attend to the general symptoms of his patient. A stormy consultation ensued. "Stop," said the first surgeon, "I will state the case to the crowd, and be governed by their instructions." "Cut it out," said the crowd, but the poor man had himself "cut out" before the doctor returned.

Many of these early doctors are yet living. I have, therefore, avoided mentioning their names for, like Dr. Atkinson of York, when I speak of live doctors "I proceed warily, skimming over them and their names, as if I were kicking a wasp."

The population of Madison County in 1830 was as great as at present. The endemics[2] consisted then, as at present, chiefly of bilious intermitting and remitting fevers during the summer and fall; continued and typhoid cases of the same, together with inflammation of the thoracic viscera in the winter and spring, but of a more grave character. It

---

[2] "Diseases which are originally engendered and propagated in certain countries as in their native soil." *Mead, Med. Works*, p. 309. *Gal. Com. Hip.* 1. *Epid. p.* 242.

was not uncommon, then, for a case of congestive bilious fever to terminate fatally in forty-eight hours; now, under fair treatment, it is very uncommon.

CASE

Two carpenters, both stout young men of about 24 years, while engaged in shingling a house on Saturday, the 21st of July last, had each a chill. The thermometer in the direct rays of the sun on the ground stood at 148°, and in the valley of the roof where they worked was much higher. Beal laid on the shavings until he felt better, then rode eight miles in the country by two o'clock, and continued riding until after night. Walker went home and laid on his bed. Beal returned Sunday night, and lay in the room with Walker. On Monday morning I saw them both, and gave each 10 grains calomel and 5 grain pulvule doses. Walker was hot, restless and silent, his surface red, tongue brown, pulse full but soft, numbering 120; he said his fever had been much higher. Beal was restless and noisy; skin pale, tongue white, pulse irritable, numbering 130. I prescribed oil, if requisite, at sundown, and left 30 grains quinine for each, to be taken in 5 grain doses one hour apart, commencing at midnight. The mercurial cathartic acted on Walker; Beal took pills (extract colocynth compound) in place of the oil at sundown, which acted. Towards midnight the fever in both cases abated. Walker took his quinine; Beal refused, though frequently urged. On Tuesday morning at eight o'clock Walker, though oppressed, was as comfortable as a very sick man could expect to be. Beal said he also felt much better, and would take his quinine directly; he was pulseless, and in less than an hour dead. Walker recovered after a severe attack. Mild, mercurial cathartics, combined with gentle ano- dynes, cold continuous affusions when the skin became hot and dry, and 15 to 20 grains of quinine daily, were employed in his case.

The temperature of the atmosphere about the head wa- ters of the "Forks of Flynt," is generally a few degrees cooler than with us, and there our earliest cases of essential and symptomatic fever take place, and linger longest; the balance of the county (except the river and creek margins) never was very sickly, and is now one of the healthiest regions in the Union. If any one who is used to topographi- cal observations will cast his eye over our diversified sur- face, he will see at a glance all that is essential to health, comfort, and long life. The boundaries of our county are mountainous, the northern part covered with immense heavy timbered flats, the central portion undulating, and the extreme south bounded by a large river that carries off the comparatively insignificant swamp water; and the whole traversed by numerous rivers, creeks, and streams that supply sufficient water for all industrial purposes. Nature has done her part, and if white men would lay their hands to the plough, and put the rich soil to the question, it would respond to "some an hundred, some sixty, some thirty fold."

Our physicians do not now use as large doses of quinine as formerly; these enormous doses, 100 grains, during the apyrexia, were introduced by Dr. Fearn in a few specific cases after anxious consideration, and were continued in the most empirical and thoughtless manner by physicians and families, and of course without a corresponding result.

CASE

A negro girl on the plantation of Mr. Fennel, in 1838, a few days after parturition, had a chill about midday; a violent fever followed, which subsided next morning. Her master, who had given her a large dose of calomel, gave her at intervals of an hour, three 20 grain doses of quinine, and with one drachm of this medicine in her the chill returned at the hour. When I saw her the same evening she was hot, dry, and restless; her pulse fluctuating, and mind wandering. I *poured* over her *slowly* two buckets of cold water; her system gradually reacted, and towards morning the fever abated. I gave her 20 grains of quinine, and directed three more doses of the same size; her master, without knowing that I had given the first, gave her another immediately; her old mistress, who had gone to look at the clock, returned and gave her a third scruple; in due time the gentleman gave her his second (4th) dose, and in a few minutes the lady gave her another (5th) dose; in another hour the girl received two more scruples. I saw her at midday; she had no chill; her surface was clammy and damp like the back of a frog; she was deprived first of her hearing, then of her vision, then of feeling, and lastly of her speech. Candles and pistols were flashed and shot about her head, and pins stuck in her. I *dashed* two or three buckets of cold water on her *suddenly*, ordered warm stimulating enemata, and wrapped her in warm blankets. In the course of the night she felt a pin scratch, at length her eyes followed a candle and she spoke; in a few days her hearing was restored. I have not for many years had occasion to give such larges doses of quinine; 15 to 25 grains I find sufficient; our diseases have moderated, or we over-dosed them. Dr. Fearn considered large doses of quinine sedative, which is certainly true, and the same may be said of large doses of brandy.

CASE

In 1835, some young gentlemen, for amusement, gave a mulatto boy of about twelve years, half a pint of strong gin; he danced about a while and sank upon the floor, cold, clammy and senseless; they carried him home and his mother sent for a "steam doctor," who gave him brandy and pepper (No. 6) and a steam bath! In the morning "the crowner set on him," and on my evidence pronounced a verdict: that, although the first dose was sufficient, it was the last drop that run the cup over.

From 1830 to 1835, our county was infested by these disciples of Thompson, calling themselves Botanic Physicians, but regularly known as "steam doctors." They were generally discontented and indolent mechanics, unemployed overseers, with a few illiterate preachers, and many respectable planters who were in the habit of thinking for themselves in politics and religion, and felt safe in entertaining their own views of physic also. The immediate evils which this class inflicted on society were chiefly among themselves, and though great, were small to the remote effects. They were the Grubs of the race, whose externals warned men at sight, and passed off with the season to go through a sort of *pupa* or *chrysalis* state, at some obscure college of quackery in Ohio, or Memphis, where they learned to smatter technicals, and returned full blown insects of various kinds, such as hydropathists, phrenologists, homœopathists, mesmerisers, half-bred regulars, and college bred steamers!

We are not subject to epidemics of any kind. The cholera has never been nearer than Fayetteville, Tennessee. The winter of 1832–3, like that of 1849, was so mild and moist that meat almost universally spoiled in the spring. Bowel complaints prevailed to a great extent during both these seasons but not a single case of cholera of which it seemed the representative.

CASE

1833. A man named Beasly, who had committed some offence in Tennessee, fled to this county, and was found dying with the cholera, where he had secreted himself from justice.

CASE

1833. On the plantation of the late Dr. James Manning, seven miles west of Huntsville, I saw twenty cases down with all the various grades of diarrhea; a fortunate application of moderate doses of calomel and opium reduced my patients to seven, and these were convalescent. The overseer, in consultation with the mistress, treated the sick to mutton soup; during the succeeding night two of the seven purged to death, and two more died during the day.

This past season the diarrhea broke out in the northeast part of the county; there has been some difficulty in its management, though but few deaths have occurred.

CASE

1849. Two negro women on the plantation of Corbin Lewis, Esq., eight miles northeast, were taken with bloody diarrhea on Tuesday. On Thursday the oldest died. On Friday I prescribed (calomel grains 10, opium grains 1, twice daily) for the other; she recovered.

CASE

1849. Every hand on Benjamin Tiller's plantation, five miles northeast, and four or five of his children, were seized in the course of a few days in May, with bloody diarrhea. I treated these cases with small doses of calomel and opium, opium alone and Dover's Powder, until the purging ceased, and applied a large blister over the abdomen. The negroes all recovered; his son, a boy of about 12 years, who refused his physic and tore off his blister, died within 48 hours of his attack. In a few days a delicate little daughter, as gentle as a lamb, was seized and carried off, leaving her parents without consolation, and her physician without excuse.

CASE

1849. On the 22d of July I saw a mulatto boy of about 18 or 20 years of age (servant of J. H. Lewis, Esq.). He had been griped all day, and taken 1 grain opium and 20 drops laudanum; about midnight he had discharged from his bowels a chamber pot half full of pure blood; he was restless, with a small, feeble pulse. I ordered a clyster of cold water; $\frac{1}{4}$ grain opium and 2 grains acetate of lead every two hours, and 3 grains tannin between the doses; bathed his abdomen in turpentine and applied a blister; before daylight he had another large discharge of blood, so pure that it clotted. The cold water clyster repeated; there was no more purging on the third; restlessness continued; mustard applied to his extremities; slept well through the night; during the day he had taken chicken water prepared after Sydenham's directions; a slight reaction in the morning gave some hopes; towards midday he became silent, then delirious, pulse failed; a profuse discharge of blood, dissolved and putrid, carried him off.

Examinations twelve hours after death. The large veins of the abdomen were as empty as the arteries; the stomach showed signs of recent and remote inflammation, in places thickened, in places softened. The entire internal surface of the intestines appeared washed, and for several feet together sprinkled over with red sanders, and occasionally stained in large patches. The follicular glands were enlarged and indurated, feeling like seed sown under the surfaces, or in the language of Baillie, "fissured upon it so as to resemble little common warts." About three feet of the termination of the ilium was unusually porous, the emunctories appearing large enough to admit a small probe.

In the Spring of 1833 we were visited by the scarlet fever in its most malignant form. During the prevalence of this epidemic more than fifty infants perished in Huntsville, at the only age they are not an annoyance here. I treated nine bad cases, and four terminated fatally; I lost nearly half in almost every instance. An older practitioner was called in, but I am not certain that in their own proper practice they were more fortunate. In more than one instance there lay more than one dead child in the same house at the same time. I feel certain that this was a most malignant disease; but I do not feel certain that in every case our best physicians remembered the united counsel of Hippocrates[3] and Ovid[4] that "nothing does good but what may also hurt," and which should never be lost sight of by the man of medicine.

With some variations of the rules laid down by Dr. Currie,[5] cold water had been skillfully and successfully used in our malignant forms of bilious fever, particularly in the different stages of that type vulgarly known by the name of "congestive fever," marked by great restlessness, a pale, shrivelled and dry surface, producing on the mind of the patient a sensation of heat, but on the hand of the physician that of cold; a compressed, irregular and wiry pulse, and a consequent congestion of some central organ. If I understand the use of cold water in these cases, it is the reaction that is desired, and if this is not effected in every instance, it does mischief. Erasmus Wilson regards cold water as a sedative, and even compares it with bella-

[3] *Lib.* 1, *Epid.*

[4] *Lib.* 4, *Trist. Mead.*

[5] The Rev. Dr. Hancock of Lothbury, recalled the attention of physicians to the use of cold water as the "*Febrifugum Magnum*" in 1722 (Bateman). This penchant of reverend gentlemen to improve the art of medicine is charitable, seeing physicians generally evince so little taste to reciprocate such favors. After this Dr. Currie of Liverpool fastened the attention of the faculty upon it by deducing certain rules for its application; the principle of which is, whenever the skin is "hot and dry."

donna and opium.[6] But this is certainly not always the case, and depends much on the mode of using it. If a patient be laid at the distance of six or eight feet, and a large bucket of cold water *dashed forcibly* over him, there is nothing sedative in it; it arouses everything to action, *if there is power left to act*. But if he be set upright in a tub, and pitcher after pitcherful of cold water poured slowly over his head and shoulders, the vital action may be reduced even to zero. This is the mode I use when the "skin is hot and dry."

With these views of the therapeutics of cold water, and the fatal treatment in the spring of 1841, I resisted its application in the second visitation of this fatal disease, because in scarlet fever there is the reverse of the state of things in congestive fever. The congestion here is on the surface—the direct action of the water is likely to be so severe as to render any reaction after it of but little service—or, if it should take place, of doubtful propriety, being in a tissue already tumid with arterial action. If it should not take place, *retrocession*, in a large majority of cases, will—and we thus fall under the censure so forcibly expressed by Rayer[7] in his great work on diseases of the

[6] Both cold affusion and belladonna appear to me to act therapeutically by virtue of their sedative effects upon the nervous system —cold affusion has been used with great advantage in fevers, and the sedative powers of opium have lately been employed in France for the purpose of checking inflammatory action.—*Diseases of the Skin*, p. 72, *London*, 1847.

[7] A benign scarlatina may nevertheless become dangerous by the retrocession of the exantheme provoked by an incendiary treatment, or by the impression of cold.—*Diseases of the Skin*, vol. 1, § 259, p. 215. *Paris*, 1835.

skin—and because, in 1836, I heard the late Baron Alibert express himself against the use of cold affusions in
scarletina in the most decided terms. These views he had
entertained and maintained through the storms incident to
an eminent Parisian' practitioner and the experience of a
long professional life, with the calmness of conscious
right not common to medical controversy, and the skill of
an accomplished philosopher; he reiterates them in the last
(2nd) edition of his splendid monograph, in a manner to
satisfy any one of his thorough conviction of their truth.[8]
He recommends warm baths, mustard foot-baths and sinap-
isms in case of interruption of the eruption. Rayer,[9] Wilson,[10] and even Bateman,[11] restrict the use of cold water
to the middle stage of the disease (S. Ang.); and though
the latter wrote of it as if he were writing the biography
of a friend, and recommended it in the very language of
Currie, he was content himself to use cold sponging of
vinegar and water, from the prejudices of mothers and

[8] Je recommende à mes élèves de ne recourir qu'avec une extreme
circonspection aux affusions d'eau froid, qui ont été préconisée de
nos jours, et qui portant ont été funestes d'apres des expériences
assez recentes.—*Monographie Des Dermatoses. p.* 248. *Paris,* 1835.

[9] D'un autre coté les Medicins qui ont le plus preconisé les lotions
et les aspersions, froides (*Currie, Withering, Bateman, Thompson*),
declarent cette varieté, (*S. Mal.*) elles ne sont point avantageuses.—
Rayer, Mal. de la Peau, tom. I. § 263, *p.* 219. *Paris,* 1835.

[10] The surface of the body may be sponged with warm vinegar,
but the use of cold water, so agreeable and beneficial in S. Ang., is
painful and injurious in the malignant form.—*Wilson, Diseases of the
Skin, p.* 73. *London,* 1847.

[11] The active remedies which act so favorably in S. Ang., es-
pecially the cold washing, are altogether out of place here.—*Bateman,
Synop., p.* 87. *Philadelphia,* 1818.

nurses. I will not say how much of his great reputation may have been preserved to him by these instinctive prejudices; but I do not hesitate to say that an opposite course of treatment, though used recklessly by a class of charlatans among us, favored the dying reputation of "steamers," and gave their friends something to boast of when compared with the "cold water" treatment.

Where there was great cerebral action and a tardy development of the eruption (S. Sine Erup.) or an unfortunate retrocession, I have placed my patients in a warm, weak, mustard bath, and after laying a blanket close round the neck and over the edges of the tub, to shed the water, poured several pitchers-full cold and slowly over the head. These are the only cases, and this the only mode that has fallen under my observation, that has not proved mischievous.

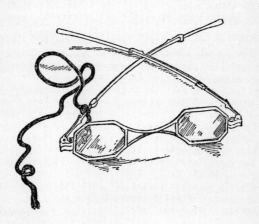

The different stages of scarlet fever having received specific names, generally receive specific treatment also— the first stage, S.S., requires none by common consent; for Rhazes, who confounded it with measles and small-pox, treated the mild cases with light diet, cool air and sub-acid drinks; and Sydenham asserts that none die except by "nimia Medici diligentia." This opinion is endorsed by the best medical authorities, living or dead, since his day, Bateman,[12] Alibert,[13] Rayer,[14] Wilson,[15] Wood,[16] &c.

In the second stage (S.A.) the battle of the waters is fought, the cold water men grow warm, and the warm water men get cool. In the third stage (S.M.) the respectable cold water authorities retire. The fourth (S.S.E.) is an incident to the other three.

If our epidemics were S.S., we fell under the censure of Sydenham. If they were S.A., the inefficiency, at least, of cold water was proved by the voice of wailing from almost every house in the village. We resembled the Egyptians at the slaying of the first-born, "for there was

[12] It is scarcely necessary to speak of the treatment of a disease which has been pronounced by great medical authority fatal only "by the officiousness of doctors."—*Bat. Synop.*, *p.* 73.

[13] Si l'exanthème suit sa marche ordinaire, on se borne à administrer quelques boissons agrèablement acidulèe.—*Alibert, mon. des Dermat, p.* 247.

[14] La S. Simp. chez un sujet bien constitue, qui n'a pas récement eprouvè des maladies aguë ou chronique, est sans danger.—*Rayer, Mal. de la Peau, tom. I., p.* 25.

[15] The treatment should be of the simplest kind, Sydenham remarks, &c.—*Wilson, p.* 70.

[16] In a vast majority of cases scarlet fever would end favorably without treatment. Hence the reputation acquired by homœopathy in this disease.—*Wood, Proc. Med. Vol. I., p.* 406. *Philadelphia,* 1847.

scarce a house where there was not one dead." If, as I have asserted, and as the graveyard testifies, a large portion of these cases were of the malignant form, the Huntsville practice must needs run the gauntlet of every respectable authority from Rhazes of the tenth century to Wood of the present day.

In the autumn of 1835 a case of small-pox appeared in our village and terminated fatally; some dozen cases followed, most of which perished. The authorities procured a temporary hospital and appointed Dr. Patton to attend it; and though he performed the severe duties of his charge faithfully, skillfully, and promptly, yet everything that he did not manage was badly managed. The provisions were but indifferent, the house open, the nurses partook of the common alarm; a cold rain prevailed; many of the patients were chilled or wet in the vehicle that conveyed them from town, and in some instances moribund on their reception at the hospital.

My treatment was pretty much that laid down by Dr. Meade: bleeding, gentle aperients, cool air, sub-acid drinks, mild anodynes, and vitriolic infusion of barks. Although the purgative part of this treatment embroiled the faculty of the early part of the 18th century to such a degree that the like had not been heard since the days of Guy Patin and Antimony—shaking the authority even of the celebrated triumvirate, Mead, Friend and Radcliffe, and who on their part embalmed one Dr. Woodward in their gall, and handed him down to posterity, like a "dried preparation," as a specimen of the folly of small men who attempt to run against "the throned opinions of the world"—and a proof that "polite literature does not always polish its possessors"—yet we of Huntsville were too willing that our brethren should have our cases, to question closely each other's practise.

Although the therapeutic treatment of small-pox has not materially varied since the days of Rhazes, who seemed to consider it as natural to man as a change of voice to adolescence, indeed an incident to this stage of life[17]—yet its prophylactic treatment is the greatest benefit the human family has ever received from any one member of the medical faculty. Such is the contagious nature of this pest that Rhazes (900 A.D.), without recognizing this cause, asserted that "except here and there one, nobody escapes it;" and such was its virulence in 1747 that the venerable Dr. Mead scorned his learned friend Boerhaave for presuming to hope "that some time or other an antidote may be found against this contagious poison" (Aph. 1390) and compared his views to the designed ravings of an alchemist.[18] In 1835, it visited a population of 2,600, immediately surrounded by 26,000; it attacked less than one in a thousand, but with the violence of Rhazes and

[17] For without doubt, as urine naturally ferments until it comes to perfection, so the blood undergoes the same alteration in passing from its first to its second state.—*Rhazes on Small-pox, Mead's Trans.,* p. 360. *Med. Works.*

[18] The principles and elements of things are so certain and so well established by the permanent laws of nature, that whosoever would endeavor to change them would act like those philosophers by fire (as they style themselves) who labor hard to transmute the baser metals into gold, and actually extract gold out of the purses of the ignorant and credulous by the fumes of their charcoal.—*Mead, Med. Works,* p. 330. *London,* 1762.

the fatality of Mead—showing its ferocious nature as a caged lion does upon a single victim that imprudently happens within its reach—which shows that Dr. Mead, though 'Physician to his late Majesty King George II' and a dignified and learned gentleman, was not a prophet; and that Dr. Jenner, though poor enough, God knows, was not the equivalent of a mountebank. And it shows another thing: that, notwithstanding alchemy, witchcraft, mesmerism, homœopathy, *et id. omne genus*, there is an imperishable germ of truth in medicine; and that there are other true medical philosophers who, when they catch a glimpse of this cynosure through the mists of quackery that obscure almost every horizon, may exclaim with Dr. Mead: *'non sibi, sed toti gentium se credere mundo.'*" (Lucan.)

The spring of 1849 commenced wet and cold, pleurisies and pneumonias prevailing. As the season advanced, diarrheas of every degree and character supervened, but not a case of cholera. Several cases of purpura occurred in the neighborhood, the first of a decided character that has fallen under my notice here.

CASE

A servant of Mr. Leftwiche, aet. about 14, who had been subject to chills for a few months, was taken with bleeding at the nose; this continued for several weeks, with more or less inconvenience. When I saw her early in June, the bleeding was so profuse that I plugged the posterior nares. Next morning the blood was oozing from the other nostril, and she had passed it from her bowels.

I gave her elixir vitrol and an infusion of bark; towards evening the blood issued from her ears, eyes, mouth, and every mucus opening in her body. She had the appearance of Lucan's child bit by the Lybian serpent, with the exception of the bloody sweat; and I am not certain that her cheeks did not sweat a colored ichor that stained her pillow, for her profile when she slept was marked in blood upon it.

> . . . . . . "So from the pores
> Of all the parts flowed ruddy venomed gore,
> . . . . . . Nature's passages,
> For their own humours were all filled with blood;
> Her mouth, her nose, choked up with filthy clots,
> Red sweat transpired from all the skin inflamed,
> Her body seemed one universal wound."—(*Lib. ix. v.* 806.)

Her very black complexion presented the appearance of discolored spots. Her pulse was feeble and skin cold. I dashed a bucket of cold water on her, wrapped her in a warm blanket, and gave her hot wine whey; a slight reaction followed, and she rested well that night. In the course of the following day the hemorrhage ceased, and she died comatose towards night. I did not open her, but believe there was an effusion in the ventricles. It was the only fatal case I heard of.

RECAPITULATION

We have less than 30,000 inhabitants and 30 physicians in the county; that is, one physician to each thousand. We collect annually about $30,000, or $1 from each citizen. This county consumes more than $10,000 worth of medicine, or 33 cents worth of physic per head. There are

50 pounds of calomel consumed yearly, which is about 30,000 doses of 12 grains each, or one dose per head; and 1,000 ounces quinine, or about 90,000 doses of 5 grains each, or three doses per head.

There has never been an instance of a physician getting rich in this town by his practice, and but few in the county. Dr. Fearn, who enjoyed the most extensive practice and greatest reputation of any one man, quit the profession to engage in commerce; so did Dr. Wyche, who had the next largest practice in the county. They are now both merchants of your city [New Orleans].

The $30,000 which the county pays her physicians is but bread, and scarce at that; and when we contemplate the 50 pounds calomel and 1,000 ounces quinine which they swallow, it reminds one of Falstaff's bill of fare: "But one half-penny worth of bread to this intolerable deal of sack."

CLINICAL REPORTS

CASE ONE

Excavation of the Tibia. W. N. Lynch, aet. 30, strong and active, a farmer and the son of a farmer, supposed that he had injured his leg while a boy, driving oxen. About 1830 his father consulted Dr. Fearn, who opened a deep seated abscess below the knee; in 1838 I opened another somewhat lower down. In 1841, suspecting a *sequestrum*, I advised an extensive operation, in search of the cause of so much suffering similar to the one about to be described. He declined at that time, as he has since informed me, on account of my apparent want of confidence in it. Ointments, bandages, pukes, purges, hydriodate of potassium etc., were resorted to, together with several small operations, such as cutting down upon the bone with a promise of certain cure.

In 1847 he renewed his application to me, expressing a willingness to have his leg amputated to relieve his sufferings, which were constant and sometimes severe unless his leg was elevated and his body depressed. I found the limb enlarged from the knee to the ankle, and a small fistulous opening about two fingers breadth below the articulation of the fibula, running into the solid structure of the tibia.

Feb. 8th, 1847. Aided by the advice and assistance of Dr. Fearn, who had retired from practice, I cut down upon the inner side of the tibia, commencing near the insertion of the *semi-tendinosus;* the integuments were laid aside by carrying the upper part of the incision in the direction of the tendinous fibers of the *sartorious*. The periosteum, thick red and sensitive, was removed, and the bone entered with a trephine; after penetrating over an inch, without indications of a cavity, the centre piece was removed with a gouge; it was compact, nearly solid; the wounded bone which was evidently a morbid structure, bled freely. The trephine was applied about an inch lower and another piece removed of the same character; this operation was continued down the limb to within two fingers breadth of the inner ankle, where a natural cavity containing healthy medulla was first met, signs of which appeared about two fingers higher up. There were seven pieces or plugs of bone removed, and the *mortise* cleaned out with a saw and gouge.

There was little left of this tibia but the hard external crust, which was cut through at the entrance of the fistulous opening, from the opposite side. The original cancellated structure of the head of the bone had solidified and was entirely removed by the gouge, through the opening below, into which the back of Bell's *Anatomy* might have been tenoned. The cavity was filled with lint and dressed with a light roller. The operation occupied nearly two hours, and was extremely painful. For the first two weeks chilly sensations and a pale condition of the wound indicated the free use of wine and bark. On the 6th of April he went home; in eight months he believed himself to be well; in twelve months he found employment, and to this time, upwards of two years, he has not complained.

After suffering without ceasing about eighteen years, he submitted to a painful and tedious operation; he has since assured me that from the moment the first piece of bone was removed, and the blood flowed, he had suffered no more of his peculiar pain, and after the wound was first dressed to the present moment he has not suffered any manner of pain. I required him to keep his bed for six months and not to walk under a year.

CASE TWO

Excavation of head of Tibia. Negro boy of Richard Pete, Esq., of Limestone County, aet. 12 or 14. I could get no other history of this case except that he had taken cold in his knee about a year previous, had suffered a great deal, lost his appetite, became ashy, and fallen off. I found the tibia enlarged and tender from the knee half way down the limb.

March 23rd, 1848. I operated in the same place and manner as in Lynch's case; found a similar, though less extensive morbid condition, the solidity being confined to the first six fingers, which was removed by the trephine and gouge. The operation lasted over thirty minutes, and was painful. The periosteum was more thickened and tender than in Case 1. The morning after the operation he asked for food, and continued to improve without constitutional treatment until the 20th of June, when he was sent home. He is believed to be well, though he is, as he always was, a delicate and strumous boy.

CASE THREE

Caries of Inferior head of Tibia. March 6th, 1849. Requested by Mr. Giles to see his son, a scrofulous boy about twelve years of age. He had suffered near a year with an enlarged ankle. A neighbor had opened it with a pocket knife. I found him very much reduced, pale, coughing, loss of appetite and temper; his right ankle anchylosed, greatly enlarged and surrounded with fistulous openings. There is a case pictured on the 110th page of Liston's *Practice of Surgery* not unlike it; such legs are generally amputated. I put him on tonics and hydriodate of potassium without advantage. I explained the nature of the case to the father and son, and proposed an operation to save the foot; it was cheerfully submitted to, though I had not expressed much confidence in it myself.

May 19th. I cut down and found the entire extremity of the tibia necrosed, a heavy callus formed round it, in which there was an oval opening the size of half a dime, through which my probe had felt the dead bone. By enlarging this opening I was enabled to remove with forceps about two inches of the tibia, including the articular extremity. This operation was not very painful. The wound was filled with lint and dressed with a scarf.

The extreme offensiveness of the suppuration gradually abated; port wine and bark continued; a few small pieces of bone passed out at the wound and one from the opposite side. He is gradually recovering his appetite and spirits; cough not troublesome; went home on the 12th of July with a better ankle than he brought, and a better prospect of recovery.

(The following case was communicated to Dr. P. F. Eve, of Augusta, on the 18th of May, which either never reached him or was not deemed suitable for the pages of his journal; I have not since heard of it.)

CASE FOUR

Rigidity of the mouth of the Womb. Friday evening, May 11th, at eight o'clock, I saw a negro woman of Mr. Ab. Sibely in hard labor, in which condition she had been since Tuesday morning, the 8th. The impediment to delivery proved to be rigidity of the os uteri. It felt like an inch hole in a piece of parchment or hard leather; a head, together with a hand or foot, presenting. The membranes broke on Tuesday morning; and again, on Thursday evening, large quantities of water flowed, and urine continued to dripple. During my examination, eruptions of fœtid gas broke from the womb; these had commenced the day before and continued through the night, followed by the passage of clots which, together with repeated vomiting, occasional purging, quick pulse, and hard, regular, agonizing labor pains, constituted the pathological condition. Gave 1½ grains opium; 10 o'clock, no alteration, except the pains, which continued hard and regular, were less excruciating. Gave warm clyster, 10 grains Dover's Powder, and ordered 10 more in an hour; 12 o'clock, no alteration, no sleep; pains continued regular, but tolerable; the mouth as hard as a bone; an effort to introduce two fingers left a crease under the nail. Gave warm clyster of starch and laudanum; 2 o'clock, no alteration; pains bearable; applied 2 drachms of chloroform on a sponge to the os, which remained as rigid as an ivory ring. She complained of its pricking her; in 15 minutes withdrew the sponge; reapplied fresh chloroform, and suffered it to remain 30 minutes, without effect. At 4 o'clock, being satisfied by the present and approaching symptoms of the danger of delay, I introduced a probe pointed bistoury, and nicked the os in two directions. The parts yielded under my finger, producing the impression of a clipped mesentery or cut drawing string; there was no further tearing; a leg came down; I sought another, and delivered a semi-putrid fœtus of about 7 months, and immediately another, with great ease. Up to the 17th instant her condition, though improving, remains critical. P.S.—I understand she since died.

My first observation on the above is that brandy, opium, ether, nitrous oxide, chloroform, are all anæsthetic agents, *and as such*, all act on the system precisely alike, differing in degree and manner only; that their anæsthetic influence is the result of intoxication, more rapidly on and off in the one case than in the other; and that the danger accompanying the effects is in the ratio of the activity or rapidity of the agent employed.

A gentleman desiring his finger lanced before the introduction of ether, drank half a tumbler of brandy; while he anticipated the operation, it had no effect upon him, and not having sufficient courage, he left my office; in a few minutes I found him in his own counting-room, drunk! and lanced his finger with little or no pain. I am satisfied that sufficient brandy to have overcome the terror he evinced at this operation would have endangered his life.

A vagabond may lay drunk a week and be proof against the torture of all the boys in the village; or swallow opium until he is insensible to the hot iron and cold water of all the doctors; and yet all the involuntary movements of heart, arteries and bowels go on, and in a few days he will arise from the curse of the serpent and walk upright among his biped brethren. I saw a woman bear a child, so drunk she did not know what she was doing, and I am sure she did not *feel* her pains.

Opium was introduced as an anæsthetic agent, from which laudanum received its wonderful name. Chloroform may be more fortunate. The most reliable anæsthetic agents, however, are a sharp knife, a clear head, and steady hand.

My second observation is on the scriptural objections to the use of these agents. It is truly humiliating to science to have to stop and rest upon her course until the dullness of the clergy can frame an excuse for an obvious truth—to see such a man as Dr. Simpson, of Edinburgh, stopping in the midst of his *labor* to chop logic by the way-side, like a monk of the 15th century, to endeavor to prove a truth at midday, by argument, which he had proven by practice in the morning, and thereby running at least a risk of losing by night what he had earned through the day. Let us examine in plain English his new translation of the Hebrew authority for the use of chloroform! and see if in getting one dent out of his turtle's egg he does not put another in.

He says: "It is surely worthy of remark and wonder that the language of the Bible is on this, as on other points, strictly and scientifically correct, and long ago made with perfect precision the very distinction which we are now-a-days only recognizing. For the Hebrew noun, *'etzebh*, distinctly signifies the muscular contraction or effort, and the nouns, *hhil* and *hhebel*, as distinctly signify the sensation of pain accompanying those efforts. Now the effort, or muscular contraction (the *'etzebh* of the curse), are left in their full and complete integrity under the state of anæsthesia; while the pangs or suffering (or *hhil*) against which the language of the curse does not bear, are alone annulled and abrogated." He here admits the woman to be cursed, which is not very obvious from the text, for this language is alone applied to the Serpent, and to the ground for Adam's sake. Now if the sorrow of conception and of parturition does not mean the nausea of the one and the labor pains of the other, I cannot understand the nature of a *curse*, because mere uterine contractions, without pain, is no more a curse than elbow contractions without rheumatism. But Dr. Simpson says: "There are abundance of 'maternal sorrows' connected with children and child-bearing in civilized women, quite independently of the actual agonies of parturition." Then the curse rests on "child-bearing, independent of parturition!" which is contrary not only to Scripture, but to nature and to universal observation.

Most barren women, like Elkanah's wife, pray in secret for children; and others, like Rachel, cry aloud, "give me children or I die"; and when at length "God hearkened to her and opened her womb," she said, "God hath taken away my reproach." Throughout the Bible we find the fruitful, and not the barren womb, the blessed. Manoah's wife praised God when her womb was opened by a stranger angel in the field, and did not sorrow until the pains of labor set in. Barrenness is only spoken of as a blessing, by a poetical license, to magnify some great calamity. The Psalmist tells us: "He maketh the barren woman to be the joyful mother of children; praise ye the Lord!" and Solomon, wiser than his father, says: "There are three things that are never satisfied—the grave, a barren womb, and the dry earth." I will add my testimony to David's: I have never seen a woman who did not rejoice at her first conception, and bear her burthen with pride and pleasure until labor set in.

Let us look a moment at the last clause of the curse— *"and he shall rule over thee."* We need not go to Hyperborean regions where, Dr. Prichard tells us, "the women are free and in Karafto rule their husbands," to find instances of the abrogation of this end of the curse. In certain Austral regions there are full as many put themselves from under it as are ever likely to escape the first clause by the aid of chloroform.

How much better would it be at once to say, when Moses recorded that in sorrow Eve should bear her children, it had no reference to chloroform, and that he was as ignorant of chemistry as Joshua was of astronomy. The Holy Bible claims to be a moral revelation. There is no evidence within its lids that any of the physical sciences was in a higher state of cultivation among the Jews than in other nations; nor am I aware that it claims any authority upon these subjects. And yet it is strange that this gifted race, that had the intellectual capacity to receive the revelation of a religion whose sublime simplicity dwarfs alike the complex grandeur of the Indian and the classic purity of the Greeks, should have left no other evidence of their greatness, and like the Greeks, retained nothing of it but its recollection.

Hoffman, who had the merit of first turning the attention of practitioners to the morbid affections of the nervous system, has been charged with having ridden his hobby to death; but as it is not my intention to arraign anew his opinions of this almighty agent in the animal economy, which seems to preside over and regulate the functions of the entire body corporal, more like a creator than a mere sovereign, I will for the present state my belief that modern physicians, in their bold treatment of the acute diseases of the South, have not always borne sufficiently in mind the possible remote effects of their heroic remedies on this mysterious, this almost spiritual organization. These convictions have been urged upon me by personal observations and reliable information on the diseases of our vicinity during the past year; and if sufficient matter be furnished me during the current year, I will in your next number refer again to this subject.

Since the fall set in, there has been but little sickness of any kind, yet the proportion of adynamic cases are perceptibly on the increase. This must be owing to some change either in the agent or the patient, the constitution of the atmosphere, or of the people; it may be to the overlapping of the choleric malaria, modified by the healthy or unhealthy atmosphere of our region; or to the normal action of indigenous causes operating on modified constitutions.

Twenty years ago, these cases were of rare occurrence, since which time two mighty agents have sprung up, each in its province calculated to effect a purpose. The atmosphere has become infectious with choleric miasma, and our systems have been charged with quinine. The enormous amount of quinine that has for the past fifteen or twenty years been consumed in this neighborhood, must have wrought an impression on the constitutions of those most subject to its influence. Numbers of cases have lately presented themselves of habitual chills, recurring every second, third or fourth day, which have required very large doses of quinine to check, and which return almost every eighth or tenth day. Since August I have treated eight successive cases of this description (in every one of which quinine had failed) with opium and plasters made of mutton suet and turpentine, or cloths dipped in warm turpentine, and applied to the pit of the stomach a half hour before the expected chill. In all these cases but one, the first chill was checked and there was no return. Although opium seems to have an excellent effect in those cases in which quinine has failed, I have sometimes succeeded with the hot turpentine cloths alone.

I was consulted in 1848 in five or six cases of night blindness that occurred in young negro men and women on one plantation, and which both the owner and myself attributed to large previous doses of quinine.

Mr. H., æt. twenty-four, who was in the habit of taking quinine freely, became typhoid in an attack of bilious pneumonia. I saw him after he had been confined ten days to his bed; his gums bled and he spat dark bloody mucus in small quantities. On the 12th of November he passed blood freely from his bowels; but opium, sugar lead, and tanin arrested it. I kept him, by the use of these direct astringents, six days without an action on his bowels, and he recovered.

Mrs. G. had five chills in five successive days, notwithstanding she had taken daily large doses of quinine (I believe from the quantity shown me from 80 to 100 grains per day). She was as yellow as buck-skin, and passing blood freely from her bowels, bladder, mouth, and nose when I saw her on the night of the 10th of December; she had no more chills. Opium, calomel and turpentine were alone used; she died on the 15th. Her skin faded nearly white on the 14th. She had lived many years on or near the river, and was accustomed to taking large doses of quinine. At the time of her death she had resided two or three years on a mountain 400 feet above the level of the town.

I am not prepared to say at present what agency, if any, quinine may have in this change of character in our maladies; and far from wishing to bring into opposition two strangers under the garb of cause and effect. This kind of logic has been rendered contemptible by quacks of every age. At present my desire is to call the attention of the profession to the facts.

December has been accompanied by an unusual number of cases of typhoid pneumonia among the negroes, who are very liable to it, and which is very fatal to them. I believe the number of cases and the relative proportion of deaths among negroes from pneumonia is many times greater than among whites, after making all reasonable allowances for the exposure of the slaves. This rule, I think, with similar allowances, is reversed in the bilious attacks of midsummer.

ARTICLE III

REPORT ON THE CLIMATE AND DISEASES OF HUNTSVILLE AND ITS VICINITY FOR THE YEAR 1850

Celsus thought it better, in doubtful cases, to try a doubtful remedy, than none at all.—IODOCUS LOMNICUS, *London edition, 1732.*

We have had but little sickness of any kind in Madison County during the past year, and for several years a perceptible decrease in our familiar forms of bilious intermitting and remitting fevers has been observed; yet we find, as these decline, a more continued type, of a lower grade of action, has appeared among us more frequently than formerly.

In the neighboring county of Limestone the actual deaths from this typhoid form of fever have possibly outnumbered those of the most seasons from bilious intermittents. In this last particular of mortality, Madison County has also been highly favored; there have been few deaths among the patients of the regular practitioners.

I have endeavored to get the best information, from the most reliable sources within my reach, on the treatment of this disease, and have found some discrepancy among our most reputable practitioners; therefore, in giving my individual experience and opinions, I desire to censure none. In such cases the best informed fear the most, and experience but renders us charitable. I will, therefore, only say that I have been fortunate, in my own practice, in reversing the aphorism at the head of this article; that rule of practice has found favor in the eyes of every generation of both doctors and patients, and it is not wonderful that the few able men of every age that have opposed it have warred in vain—that the science of French expectancy, and the quackery of German Homœopathy, have alike failed: dying men will have pills and parsons.

When physicians were required by public opinion to follow the dictates of Hippocrates, and his immediate successors, as closely as Christians now profess to follow the commandments of Moses and the prophets, they claimed a right to act boldly their faith in these authorities, and public opinion sustained them; and however difficult the task, they found it much easier to understand the written language of Hippocrates than the yet more obscure teachings of Nature, between which and his followers he stood an infallible interpreter, making her mysteries so plain that wayfaring men, though fools, could not err therein. Hippocrates was but our fellow-servant and we are but ministers of Nature; our whole art consists in understanding her language and laws; our whole practice in obeying her mandates. If we do not understand them, it is either our fault or misfortune; to act as though we did is quackery. Celsus says, this bold practice of old, *fere quos ratio non restituit temeritas adjuvat;* but shrewdly remarks that 'Physicians of this sort diet other men's patients more happily than their own.' I doubt, however, if in the present state of Medicine a thorough physician is ever in any stage of any disease so completely without rational education as to be thus nonplussed, and driven to the necessity of dealing a blow in the dark; where there are no intelligible indications it is clear there should be no action.

Then, if I have not followed the advice of this master, it has not been lightly laid aside; nor, as I have stated, without precedent; and if I have, in a measure, adopted another of his rules, to make food physic (*optimum vero medicamentum est, cibus datus*) it has not been upon his mere authority. I revere authority, believing with the royal preacher that 'whoso breaketh a hedge, a serpent shall bite;' yet I rejoice that its fetters are broken in Medicine—that we no longer are hedged in with the eternal cry of 'Hippocrates and reason.' But if, in getting rid of the authority of the Ancients, we have discarded the example of their labor and learning, and turned a deaf ear to their opinions, it is easier to be lamented than corrected. If the unthinking part of the profession of old that followed authority, and 'on the first day of a fever loosened the belly, on the next opened a vein, on the third give a bolus' etc., are now represented by those who follow fashion, and give calomel, quinine and cod-liver oil every day, we have but changed authority for fashion, and are yet in bondage. But fashion, though indomitable, changes with the wind, and if for a time it carries the small craft, the weak or designing in its current, it soon leaves them stranded, as land-marks, at which we can at least laugh without fear of professional martyrdom.

I do not say there is no virtue in cod-liver oil, but I do say from very limited experience and some reflection, that there is more for a consumptive in good fat mutton (bating the mystery which will soon abate itself, and the trace of iodine which is at least useless here)[1]. I have never seen a poor hectic swallow her nauseous dose of semi-putrid train oil and retain it under a sort of superstitious influence, which is the prime virtue in all nostrums, that I have not felt humbled in my profession; nor is it wonderful that this delicate creature, who has been starved for months on black tea and toast, should suddenly improve on the addition to her daily food of six or eight ounces of animal oil; it would be more charitable, however, and more sensible,

---

[1] Since the foregoing remarks were written, we trust cod-liver oil has found more favor in the sight of the worthy author. On account of pulmonary disease he was, last winter, compelled to seek the more genial climate of Florida, and as he passed through this city on his return in March (much improved, we are happy to say) we urged him to give the cod-liver oil a fair trial in his own case. We have not heard from him since he reached home, but sincerely hope he may have realized all the benefit that ever was claimed for this now popular remedy.—ED.

to make physic of more palatable food. Any article of the *materia medica* used superstitiously or exclusively, is quackery. Calomel and quinine thus used are as much quackery as the water of the Hydropathist, which being also an article of our *materia medica* from the time of Galen, is only quackery when thus used.

Although the present century has added several new agents to our vast catalogue of remedies that have not belied their inventors, I contend that there is no present need of further additions, but much of liberal curtailment. Celsus tells us of 'a certain Petro,' ancient in his days, whose whole park of munitions consisted of *blankets, cold water, roast pork*, and *wine;* to which modest limits I would not care to be restricted, but think, somewhere between Don Petro of ancient days and Bache of modern, might be profitably selected.

I have said that we are ministers of Nature, and will add, necessary to her in Medicine. Nature has no power to replace a dislocated member and needs the assistance of a surgeon, whose function ceases when it is reduced, and then she displays wonderful powers in consummating a cure. Our mission is special, and we should not usurp plenipotentiary privileges, but walk humbly in our vocation, claiming only that power which we possess; and to possess any real power in Medicine, the language of Nature must be studied in her normal actions. This is Physiology, the foundation of all medical knowledge, without a proper understanding of which we can never be but respectable empirics, which is certainly a more useful and respected character than that of the pretender to science, who has neglected to appreciate his experience. The public generally acknowledge this, but the profession is not often laid under obligations by this respected class of physicians, who generally yield to the fondness of their patients for new remedies, and thus secure a character for liberality at the hazard of weakening the public faith in the science of their profession when the compliment should rest where it is merited.

I do not say that the study of nature, human and comparative, so far as it relates to medicine, is an easy task. Let any one undertake a foreign language, and when he thinks he has mastered it, let him go into its native country and attempt to use it among the polite and well-informed. If he succeed, let him go among the illiterate and rude where slang is current; into the lunatic asylum, where the vernacular is babbled in broken sentences through the mouth of an idiot, and attempt to understand this. Should he again succeed, he may safely say that he knows that language. Let him then set down and calculate the cost in labor, time, and talent; then square this amount and go boldly into the study of physiology; and when he has exhausted his programme, he will find himself humbly knocking at the door of the Temple, and it will be opened. For diligence, like the vinegar of Hannibal, will make a way through frozen Alps; it is the 'open sesame' of our profession. When he is satisfied with the beautiful proportions of the interior, its vast and varied dimensions, the intricate and astounding action of its machinery, obeying laws of a singular stability, whose very conflict produces harmony under the government of secondary laws (if there be anything secondary in nature!); when he is satisfied (and such are not satisfied until informed) he will be led to his ultimate object, to take his last lessons from the poor and suffering, the fevered and phrenzied, from the Jobs and Lazaruses, into the pest-houses and prisons, and here, in these magazines of misery and contagion, these Babels of disease and sin, he must not only take up his abode but, following the example of his Divine master, he must love to dwell there. This is Pathology.

When such an one reenters the world, he is a physician; his vast labors have not only taught him how little he knows, but that he knows this little well. Conscious of this virtue, he feels no necessity of trumpeting his professional acquirements abroad, but with becoming modesty and true dignity, which constitute genuine professional pride, he leaves this to the good sense of his fellow-citizens to discover.

The evident change in our diseases, that has been in progress of late years, argues a change either in the agent or patient, the climate in its most extensive signification, or in the constitution of the people, which last approaches so near an absurdity that I have taken the first only into consideration in these brief remarks.

I have annexed[2] a carefully revised meteorological table, including five years' observations from 1830, and compared it with observations made during 1850, in which I find not a mere accidental discrepancy, but an apparent permanent change in the climate. We find the monthly mean temperature in every instance greater in 1850, which contradicts the popular opinion that our climate is getting colder. We also find the extreme monthly and daily variations of the thermometer less in every instance, which gives us a reason, if correctly stated, for the universal opinion that Madison County has grown more healthy of late years. The number of rainy days in 1850 is nearly double the average of the other five years, and the amount of rain fifty per cent greater, which contradicts the general opinion that our dry years are healthy (it is more true when confined to seasons); 1850, which has been remarkably healthy, had its due portion of rain, with the exception of the Fall months. I give the above as a statement of a possible cause, among others, of the change of our maladies, without pretending to be satisfied with it as an explanation of the phenomena.

The first cases of typhoid, mucous, or nervous fever that

[2] Dr. Bassett sent us an abstract from the meteorological tables of the late Rev. John Allen, of Huntsville, for the years 1830–'35, inclusive, to which he appended an abstract for 1850, which we are compelled to leave out for two reasons: first, because we are forced to abridge our table-work in this volume, and secondly, because we do not think there can be a perfectly fair comparison between *one* year of a certain period and *five* of another. We will insert the general summary of Dr. Allen's observations and Dr. Bassett's abstract for the year 1850, which is the best we can do.—Ed.

occurred to me was some time during the spring and summer of 1835; at that time it was called *winter fever* in winter, and *slow fever* in summer. I did not understand it. The symptoms were obscure, as at present: a slight pain below the right ribs, dry tongue, moderate pulse, and some restlessness; an occasional chill, repeated irregular rigors, with partial sweats that seemed to give no relief; and these symptoms seemed to hold their course independent of all treatment. As the disease determined itself, the bowels generally became loose, giving issue to mucous discharges, the urine copious, and either the lungs or brain involved. It was impossible for me to say at what time the patient got worse. The eyes become watery and averse to the light, and are closed either from an inability or reluctance to open them; the hearing becomes dull, and the articulation gets from under the control of the will (I do not allude to the muttering, or sleep-talking, but to the inability of the patient to say what he wishes). I know of no certain sign of sinking. I have seen them recover from every stage, which has been so gradual that I never could tell for several days whether they were improving or not. These two changes, of worse and better, have bewildered me more than anything that has presented itself to me in the practice of Medicine; but when every one sees that the patient is better—the doctor admits it; he begins to desire food, his appetite becomes voracious, it is ungovernable in the most discreet and prudent, and a dangerous stage for negroes. I have lost several in this stage of recovery, after I had ceased to visit them, by a gorge of food clandestinely given

METEOROLOGICAL OBSERVATIONS FOR 1850 AT HUNTSVILLE, ALABAMA

Months	Barometer			Thermom. attached			Thermometer, exposed					Days					Amount of rain	Wind
	Highest	Lowest	Monthly Mean	Highest	Lowest	Monthly Mean	Highest	Lowest	Monthly Mean	Extreme Daily Variations	Extr. Mo'ly Variations	Clear	Cloudy	Rainy	Windy	Stormy		
January . .	31st, 29°84	20th, 29°13	29°51	31st, 84°	5th, 37°	60½°	9th, 85°	1st, 18°	51°	9th, 32–85 = 53°	67°	10	21	16	3	3	12 ins.	E., SE., NW.
February.	5th, 29°96	13th, 28°	29°45	28th 75°	4th, 40°	55½°	26th, 98°	4th, 6°	50°	7th, 34–82 = 48°	92°	15	13	10	3	1	5.740	S., SE., SW.
March . . .	4th, 29°70	6th, 29°12	29°42	14th, 78°	27th, 41°	59¾°	14th, 95°	28th, 30°	58½°	24th, 82–32 = 50°	66°	20	11	8	3	7	9.550	N., SE., SW.
April	23d, 29°60	5th, 28°94	29°39	22d, 80°	27th, 47°	62°	29th, 100°	6th, 44°	64°	14th, 92–46 = 46°	56°	17	13	11	9	. .	8.650	S., N., SW.
May	1st, 29°71	15th, 29°10	29°40	27th, 90°	6th, 55°	71°	26th, 118°	6th, 50°	71°	26th, 118–65 = 53°	68°	21	10	9	6	. .	8.700	N., E., SW.
June. . . .	. . . .	. . . .	. . . . . .	. . . .	. . . .	. . . .	22d, 116°	12th, 59°	71°	11th, 108–62 = 46°	57°	19	11	8	. .	. .	3.500	S., N., E.
July	26th, 29°59	22d, 29°36	29°47½	18th, 84°	21st, 66°	80°	11th, 135°	7th, 60°	84¾°	7th, 130–60 = 70°	75°	16	15	13	. .	. .	4.450	E., SE., SW.
August . . .	2d, 29°62	24th, 29°27	29°47	15th, 90°	26th, 75°	86¼°	8th, 135°	30th, 66°	86¼°	9th, 130–70 = 60°	105°	19	12	10	. .	3	9.300	NW., N., NE.
September	3d, 29°60	19th, 29°30	29°48½	26th, 82°	2d, 68°	75°	26th, 120°	3d, 50°	81°	11th, 112–56 = 56°	70°	26	4	3	. .	. .	0.850	NE., S., E.
October.	28th, 29°75	18th, 29°26	29°53	5th, 79°	27th, 50°	65°	15th, 114°	27th, 25°	70¼°	27th, 92–27 = 65°	89°	20	11	1	. .	. .	0.200	NW., S., SW.
November	7th, 29°80	28th, 29°31	29°56	2d, 70°	18th, 40°	56¼°	3d, 112°	18th, 14°	57¼°	3d, 112–53 = 59°	98°	20	10	5	2	. .	4.000	SW., SE., N.
December	8th, 29°80	22d, 29°00	29°54½	3d, 66°	9th, 37°	51°	2d, 85°	9th, 15°	49¼°	11th, 78–20 = 58°	70°	12	19	11	2	1	8.450	N., S., NE.
						65⅔			66⅙			215	150	105	28	15	75.390	SW., E., S.

GENERAL SUMMARY OF THE METEOROLOGICAL OBSERVATIONS MADE BY THE LATE REV. JOHN ALLEN OF HUNTSVILLE, ALA., FOR FIVE YEARS (1830 TO 1835) AND BY J. Y. BASSETT, M.D., IN 1850

Annual mean of the sum of the mean temperature from 1831 to 1835. . . . . $717°$

Sum of the mean temperature of 1850 . . . . $792°$

Annual mean of the sum of the extreme monthly variations of temperature, 1831 to 1835 . . . . $524°$

Sum of the extreme monthly variations of temperature, 1850 . . . . $355°$

Annual mean of the sum of the extreme daily variations of temperature, 1831 to 1835. . . . . $331°$

Sum of the extreme daily variations, 1850 . . . . . $249°$

Amount of rainy days during 1831 to 1835 284

Annual average of rainy days, 1831 to 1835. . . . . 56.80

Amount of rainy days during 1850 105

Amount of rain, in inches, 1831 to 1835 . . . . . . 282.271 in.

Annual average of rain, 1831 to 1835 . . . . 56.454 "

Amount of rain, in inches, 1850. . . . . 75.390 "

Prevailing winds during 1831 to 1835 . . . . . N.W. and S.W.

Prevailing winds during 1850. . . . . S. and E. and S.W.

by their parents or friends. They sunk within forty-eight hours from purging. Frequently the lungs are involved from the onset—then it is called *typhoid pneumonia*.

When I first treated this disease I gave calomel and quinine freely, together with opium and blisters. Seeing no benefit from this treatment, I became doubtful of its propriety, and not knowing what to do, I boldly determined to do nothing, or nearly so. After the lapse of a few years we became accustomed to this malady and relied on experience, an experience that has wrought very different effects in the minds of different practitioners. Some of those who gave large doses of calomel and quinine are confirmed in the propriety of their course; others who, like myself, were early convinced of the impropriety of this treatment, it has established in their minds the correctness of their opinions. I have therefore applied to reliable sources for information out of the profession. One gentleman, who has suffered in his own family by ten bad and many mild cases, three of the early ones proving fatal, told me that he believed he would have lost the whole ten but for a fortunate change of treatment to a more mild, nurse-like attention. He had two of the best physicians in the country, and they differed as to the general treatment, but the owner and father leaned to the milder mode. And I believe these very cases confirmed both those gentlemen in their own views, even to the treatment, the one of himself, the other of his family, according to them.

My present general treatment is to give moderate doses of blue mass and morphia, or Dover's Powder, and if it need assistance, a very small dose of oil with a few drops of turpentine; to endeavor to control the purging with laudanum and starch injection; cup the abdomen and cover it with mustard, to be removed as soon as it makes the patient restless; panada, boiled milk, chicken water, to be given with or without appetite; cold water, if it lays comfortably upon the stomach, and occasional sponging with the same. When they begin to recover, I give wine in moderation, and a little solid food, such as stewed birds or fresh meats.

When this disease rages it attacks all ages, sexes and colors, but with us it has generally been confined to young people, and been rather more fatal among blacks than whites.

The original tables of Dr. Allen contain nothing more than a faithful record of the state of the weather from three daily observations made at morning, noon and evening, and were from 1829 to 1842, occupying near fourteen half quires of foolscap (the two first years without note of rain). With much labor and some care, I reduced them to twelve tables, each covering but little more than half a page, from which I have made the above abstract. I registered the state of the weather during 1850 with great care, and for the purpose of comparing with the above; therefore used the same modes of observation, having my thermometer, like his, in a freely ventilated passage. But wishing to go further, I used two others, one exposed to the sun, the other shaded in the open air; also, a barometer, on which I made midnight observations.

This book, THE MEDICAL REPORTS OF JOHN Y. BASSETT, M.D., The Alabama Student, with an Introduction by Daniel C. Elkin, M.D., was composed, printed, and bound by The Collegiate Press of Menasha, Wisconsin. Designed by Reinhold Frederic Gehner. Illustrations by Marjorie Nielsen Gehner and Kathleen E. Mackay. One thousand copies were printed on Fairbanks rag paper, and bound in Master of Arts Green for side papers and Linweave Japan for the back strip. The type face is Monotype Janson 401 ten on twelve-point, in a type page size 20×32 picas.

AN APPENDIX: A LETTER FROM DOCTOR CLAUDIUS H. MASTIN TO DOCTOR OSLER ON INCIDENTS IN THE LIFE OF JOHN Y. BASSETT

Mobile, April 13, 1896

My dear Dr. Osler: A friend of mine greeted me in the street a few days since with the question, "Mastin, do you know Osler?" Upon my assurance that I had that pleasure he said, "Well, then I wish you to read a little pamphlet which he has sent to me." The paper in question is entitled *An Alabama Student* and has interested me exceedingly; the more so, because you have told a truthful story of a man who was far above the ordinary line of men we meet in everyday life, and one whose memory you have rescued from oblivion. I knew him intimately, and to him I owe much of what little success I have met in the rugged pathway of professional life. It so happened that in 1846, just after I had completed my academic studies at the University of Virginia, I returned to my home in Huntsville, Ala. Having decided to make Medicine my profession, I looked around for a preceptor who would mark out the proper course for me to take, and after due investigation, I concluded that Dr. John Y. Bassett was, by all odds, the best fitted man in that town to give me the instruction I required. Thus it was that I entered his office as a pupil in 1846 and remained with him eighteen months, when he advised me to go to the University of Pennsylvania and gave me a letter of introduction to his personal friend Prof. Geo. B. Wood. That letter was the means through which I became (with Busey and Hunt of Philadelphia) a private student in the office of Dr. Wood. Often times have I heard him speak in the highest terms of Dr. Bassett, and I am assured that he entertained for him the warmest regard. This was a great deal to say of Dr. Wood, for he was notably a cold and distant man, one not given to commendatory words.

It may be interesting for you to know more of Dr. Bassett than was possible for you to gather from his letters to his family when a student in Paris; and so I venture to tell you something of his early life, and the trials through which he passed—trials which hampered genius and made it impossible for him to occupy the position which by right he should have taken in the profession.

Dr. Bassett was a Marylander by birth, and was one of three brothers and a sister. His elder brother William, I believe, was an officer in the Navy; his brother Frank an apothecary; the sister, Margaret, a maiden lady of advanced age, a woman of education, *disappointed hopes* and endowed with a liberal share of bitter sarcasm, was a weight which hung upon John, and influenced his success in his profession; she was a terror to the community, the bitterness of her tongue stirred up strife, and her brother had to bear the brunt of it all. With his brother Frank, he came to Huntsville and opened a drug store. Frank was the apothecary, whilst his brother John combined the practice of Medicine with the selling of drugs. Frank met with an accident one day whilst gunning, and lost his life from tetanus induced by the bursting of his gun. The drug store passed into other hands, and Dr. Bassett became one of the regular physicians of the town.

Contrary to your conceived opinion, Huntsville was at that time one of the most refined communities in the South. Beautifully located in one of the most picturesque sections of the Union, it was peopled by a refined and wealthy class, which claimed its lineage from the Cavalier blood of Virginia and the Huguenots of Carolina, chiefly wealthy planters whose families resided in Huntsville whilst their estates of cotton, rice, and sugar were cultivated in southern Alabama, Mississippi and Louisiana. Huntsville was their residence on account of its healthful climate, and the educational advantages offered by the schools. Here the children were reared until old enough to be sent to college, and then the boys were sent to Yale, to Harvard, Princeton, or preferably to the University of Virginia.

Such was the community in which our friend had cast his fortunes: a stranger without the prestige of a name, or the influence of money, necessarily had a rough road before him; and since an influential firm, composed of Drs. Fearn, Erskine & Russel, catered to the fashion and elegance of the community, and gathered in its shekels, our friend drew his scanty support from the denizens of the hills, hollows, and caves of the surrounding country. As might be supposed, he had ample leisure, and an abundance thereof; but he was improving his time by storing his mind with useful information. Besides the study of his profession, he was a student of nature, and the bent of his inclinations led him to cognate sciences. He became deeply interested in ethnological studies, and through them arose his intimacy with E. D. Fenner of New Orleans and Blanch Dowler. His mind became warped in that direction, and hence it was he became an absolutely *free thinker* upon all subjects pertaining to science, politics and religion. Such a character was not calculated to secure the patronage of a community which was aristocratic in its origin, and bigoted in its religious sentiments. Our friend was considered a materialist in his views, an infidel in his belief, and as a consequence was endured rather than sustained. His practice yielded him a scanty support, yet, by frugality and strict economy, he garnered up a small sum and laid it aside for his European trip, long contemplated, and at last realized.

After about a year spent abroad he returned to Huntsville and opened an office. In those days few medical men from the States had taken advantage of foreign schools, and as a consequence the people were inclined to think that a man who had been to Paris and London "knew it all," and so it was with Dr. Bassett. He was by degrees introduced into a better class of practice by reason of "consultation," called for by other physicians! Thus it was the scope of his practice widened and although never a lucrative one, it became ample for his support, and his family enjoyed more of the comforts with many of the luxuries of life.

His knowledge of Anatomy and his preferences for surgery gave him the surgical cases of that section of the country and he soon became the recognized surgeon of North Alabama. There being no surgeon of ability nearer than Dr. Dudley of Lexington, Ky., Dr. Bassett was the one who did the largest amount of operative work in all the country around, and through it accumulated some considerable means. But he never enjoyed the confidence and respect of the community at large, and chiefly on account of the opposition he met at the hands of his co-workers in the profession. Besides, as I have before said, his sister, under whose influence he was largely dominated, did much to hamper his progress in his profession.

I well remember that when I entered his office as a student of Medicine, it caused much comment in the little town. Two of my brothers had married daughters, respectively of Drs. Fearn and Erskine, and as my father was one of the oldest and most influential of the citizens, it was considered very strange that I should have selected Dr. Bassett as a preceptor! But I thought differently. I knew that he was a student himself, and with the advantages of a large and well selected library, I was confident that it would be more to my interest to read under his tuition than in the office of one who had neither the time nor the ability to instruct me. My observation whilst a college student in Virginia had impressed me with the conviction that the outcome of a man depends more, as a general thing, on his first preceptor than on any subsequent instructor, for it is from him that he acquires the mental habitudes which subsequently lead him on to accuracy and distinction or to the looseness and inaccuracy with the necessary failure that these faults involve. The wisdom of my action has been verified by the subsequent history of my life.

Hence it is that I have been so interested in your sketch of the man who, though voiceless, has left an echo, responsive in your heart, as it has been in mine! Pardon this trespass upon your time, and overlook this hurried note, which is longer than I proposed to make it when I sat down to thank you for the pleasure your sketch has given me.

With kindest regards to your good wife, and assurances of my sincere regards, I am faithfully

CLAUDIUS H. MASTIN

P.S. Send me a copy of your article. I wish to preserve it!

The Appendix supplies information about John Y. Bassett which Sir William Osler lacked at the time he wrote An Alabama Student *(Johns Hopkins Hospital Bulletin, 1896). The Mastin letter is published through the courtesy of Dr. W. W. Francis, Librarian of the Osler Library, McGill University, Montreal, Canada.*

This book, THE MEDICAL REPORTS OF JOHN Y. BASSETT, M.D., The Alabama Student, with an Introduction by Daniel C. Elkin, M.D., was composed, printed, and bound by The Collegiate Press of Menasha, Wisconsin. Designed by Reinhold Frederic Gehner. Illustrations by Marjorie Nielsen Gehner and Kathleen E. Mackay. One thousand copies were printed on Fairbanks rag paper, and bound in Master of Arts Green for side papers and Linweave Japan for the back strip. The type face is Monotype Janson 401 ten on twelve-point, in a type page size 20×32 picas.

With THOMAS BOOKS careful attention is given to all details of manufacturing and design. It is the publisher's desire to present books that are satisfactory as to their physical qualities and artistic possibilities and appropriate for their particular use. THOMAS BOOKS will be true to those laws of quality that assure a good name and good will.